Progress with Oxford

Grammar, Punctuation and Spelling

Ages 8-9

Hello, I'm Art.

I'm Ickle.

Contents

OXFORD
UNIVERSITY PRESS

Plural or possessive -s

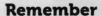

An apostrophe in front of an s shows possession.

Remember
The letter **s** at the end of a word can have different meanings.
The **s** may show the word is plural (more than one):

There were two spotted **dogs**.

The **s** may show possession (ownership):

The white cat looked like **Jasmine's**. It could be **hers**.

But a pronoun like **hers** doesn't need an apostrophe!

1 Choose the correct 'plural' or 'possession' sticker for these -s words.

a The **school's** pet day had started.

c Rio could easily lose **his**.

b There were **animals** everywhere.

d **Rio's** snake had escaped.

2 Use each word from the box to fill the gaps.

~~Finn's~~   teacher's   snakes   cats   hers

a _Finn's_ shy tortoise hid under a mat.

b Two _____ flew at each other.

c One girl had to pull _____ away.

d Four _____ hissed and frightened the teacher.

e The _____ face looked furious.

Give yourself a sticker

Check
Check that you have **not** put an apostrophe with a plural or a possessive pronoun.

2

Now – track how you're doing on page 31!

The letters ch in words

Remember

The letters **ch** make three different sounds in words.

They can sound like the ch in **ch**at.

They can sound like k as in e**ch**o.

They can sound like sh as in ma**ch**ine.

A chauffeur drives people around.

1 Say these words aloud and write them in the correct set.

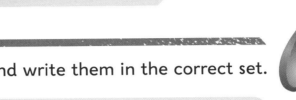

~~chrome~~   chimney   character   parachute
school   lunch   brochure   cheese   chauffeur

ch as in **chat**	ch as in **echo**	ch as in **machine**
	chrome	

2 Write a sentence using the word **anchor**.

_____

_____

3 Write a sentence using the word **parachute**.

_____

_____

Check

Check that you can say the three sounds that ch make. ☐

3

The letter y inside a word

1 Write three words beginning with **y**.

_____   _____   _____

2 Say the words in the box and listen for the **ee** and **igh** sounds made by **y**. Write the words next to the correct headings.

| fly   lucky   cry | **ee sound** _____ _____ _____ |
| funny   sorry   dry | **igh sound** _____ _____ _____ |

3 Put the missing **y** in these words. Then say the words and match them to their meanings.

m_y_th   a puzzle

Eg___pt   an exercise room

p___ramid   an African country

m___stery   a story about gods and goddesses

g___m   a structure with a base and triangular, sloping sides

> Try using a dictionary. It helps you find the spelling and the meaning of words.

Check
Check that you know the sound **y** makes inside a word. ☐

The sound made by the letters ou

Remember

The letters **ou** in words can make the sound **oo** as in s**ou**p.

The letters **ou** can also make the sound **ou** as in m**ou**th.

1 Read these words aloud. Then write them in their sound groups.

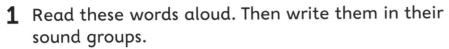
round   group   troupe   sound

ou sound

_____

_____

oo sound

_____

_____

I love making a loud sound!

Remember

The letters **ou** can also make a different sound that is more like **u**:

young   country

2 Write the answers to these clues using the **ou** words in the box.

trouble   double   country   touch   young

I'm better at solving clues than Sherlock Holmes!

a the opposite of old   _____

b twice as much   _____

c put your hand on   _____

d an area of land   _____

e a bit of bother   _____

Give yourself a sticker

Check

Check that you know the three different sounds made by **ou**.

Using prefixes: il- , ir-, inter-, super-

1 Choose the correct sticker to give these words their opposite meaning.

legible   logical   rational

relevant   regular   literate

2 Write the words you have made in the correct column.

words beginning with **il**   words beginning with **ir**

_____   _____

_____   _____

_____   _____

3 Write a rule that explains which words use which prefix.

_____

_____

_____

_____

Check

Check that you understand the effect the prefixes **il-** and **ir-** can have.

Remember
The prefix **inter-** means **between**. The prefix **super-** means **above**.

> Supercharged, that's me!

4 Use the words from the box below to complete the paragraph.

> supercharged   superhuman   supersonic   superman

Zog had amazing powers. His strength, greater than any ordinary

person's, was _____. His booster rocket pack was

_____, so that he could fly at _____ speed.

It was not surprising that others called him _____.

5 Write a sentence including the word **supernatural**.

_____

_____

6 Match these words to their meanings.

international		between cities
intercity		between countries
interchange		system of radio communication between people
interaction		a junction between roads
intercom		communication between two people and their effect on each other

> Use a dictionary to help you!

Give yourself a sticker

Check
Check that you understand the effect the prefixes **inter-** and **super-** can have. ☐

The endings -sure, -ture, -(t)cher and -cian

Remember
The word endings **-sure** and **-ture** may be similar in spelling but they make different sounds. You can hear the **s** at the beginning of **-sure** in the word **pleasure**.

1 Join the pieces to make words, then write the words underneath.

mea   ture   pic   sure

trea   sure   lec   ture

furni   sure   plea   ture

Words ending in -ture

_____

_____

_____

Words ending -sure

_____

_____

_____

2 Choose a word from the box to complete each sentence in the story. Notice the ending of each word.

a The gate to the ____*nature*____ reserve was open.

b It was a _____ to have my friend for tea.

c The sheep were in the _____.

d I swim at the _____ centre.

e The sailor had an _____ at sea.

f The platypus is a strange looking _____.

leisure

adventure

~~nature~~

pleasure

creature

pasture

Check
Check that you can hear the difference between words ending in **-sure** and words ending in **-ture**. ☐

8

Remember

The word endings **-ture**, **-tcher** and **-cher** can sound the same.

3 Choose a sticker to complete each word.

frac ☐   tea ☐   ri ☐

stre ☐   pos ☐   ca ☐

4 Write a sentence including the word **posture** or **stretcher**.

_____

_____

Remember

The word ending **-cian** is common and always sounds the same:

musician   technician

Use the **-cian** suffix if the root word ends in **c** or **cs**.

5 Choose a word from the box to complete each sentence in the story.

technician   electrician   magician   mathematician

The party entertainer was a _____.

He could add up card numbers like a _____.

Next, he turned himself into a computer _____

and mended the children's laptop. Then, as a qualified

_____, he rewired everything

and made keys glow and lights flash off and on!

Check

Check that you can say and spell the word endings **-sure**, **-ture**, **-(t)cher** and **-cian**.   ☐

Give yourself a sticker

Now – track how you're doing on page 31!

Suffixes beginning with vowels

Remember

A word may change its spelling when a suffix is added: refer + ing

Is the last syllable of the word emphasised or stressed? refer

Does the last syllable end in a consonant? refer

Is there a single vowel letter in front of the consonant? refer

If you answer **Yes** to each question, then double the consonant when you add an ending beginning with a vowel: refer + ing ⟶ referring

And there's the vowel 'e' in front of it!

1 Circle the final two letters in these words.

forget   refit

admit   begin

The final letter is a consonant.

2 Write the missing words. Remember to double the consonant.

a forget + ing → *forgetting*

d forgot + en → _____

b begin + er → _____

e prefer + ed → _____

c begin + ing → _____

f prefer + ing → _____

3 Write sentences including two of the new words you have made.

_____

_____

_____

_____

Remember

Is the last syllable of the word unstressed (not emphasised)? order

Does the last syllable end in a consonant? order

Is there a single vowel letter in front of the consonant? order

If you answer **Yes** to each question, then do **not** double the consonant when you add an ending beginning with a vowel: order + ing ⟶ ordering

---

4 Underline the final unstressed syllable in these word. Circle its final consonant letter.

> garden   limit   novel   pardon

---

5 Write the missing words. Remember **not** to double the consonant.

a garden + er → *gardener*

b novel + ist → _____

c garden + ing → _____

d trumpet + er → _____

e limit + ed → _____

f limit + ation → _____

---

6 Write a sentence including the word **limited** or **novelist**.

_____

_____

_____

_____

Give yourself a sticker

Now – track how you're doing on page 31!

The word endings -gue and -que

Remember

Although the word endings **-gue** and **-que** look similar, each makes a different sound.

-gue makes a **g** sound: league

-que makes a **k** sound: antique

1 Underline the words that end with a **g** sound. Circle the words that end with a **k** sound.

rogue	meringue	cheque	vague
technique	plague	unique	arabesque

2 Write **-gue** or **-que** to finish these words.

ton_____   fati_____   dialo_____

bouti_____   mos_____   prolo_____

3 Match these words and meanings.

picturesque   a ballet movement

unique   making a striking picture

arabesque   the only one of its kind

antique   cannot be seen through

mystique   old-fashioned

opaque   atmosphere of mystery

The -que ending comes from the French language.

Give yourself a sticker

Check

Can you make the sounds to match the **-gue** and **-que** endings? ☐

Now – track how you're doing on page 31!

The letter groups ei and ey

Remember
The letter groups **ei** and **ey** can make an **ai** sound: rein they

1 Write **ei** or **ey** in the empty squares to solve
the crossword clues.

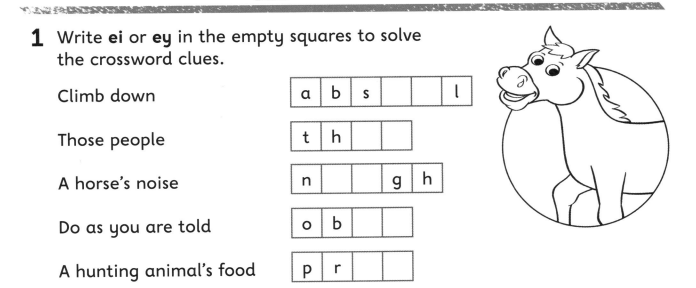

Climb down

a	b	s			l

Those people

t	h		

A horse's noise

n			g	h

Do as you are told

o	b		

A hunting animal's food

p	r		

2 Write sentences including the words **weigh**, **grey** and **sleigh**.
Circle the letter groups making the sound **ai**.

_____

_____

_____

_____

_____

_____

Check
Check that you have used the correct letter groups in
your sentences. ☐

Give yourself a sticker

Now – track how you're doing on page 31!

Apostrophes to mark possession

Remember

- The apostrophe may be a short way to show ownership. It is quicker and easier to write the **cat's** tail

  rather than the tail belonging to the cat

  or the tail of the cat.
- The apostrophe is placed with the owner. In the example above, the owner is **the cat**.
- The apostrophe's position varies depending on the owner.
  - If the owner is singular, add **'s**: the **dog's** bowl (the owner is one dog)
  - If the owner is plural and ends in s, add an apostrophe after the **s**:

    the **dogs'** bowl (the owners are two or more dogs)

1 Rewrite the sentences, using an apostrophe + s ('s or s') to make the underlined phrase shorter.

a <u>The cage belonging to the tiger</u> was empty.

The tiger's cage was empty.

b <u>The engine of the car</u> had stopped.

c <u>The name of the book</u> did not make sense.

d <u>The noise from the dogs</u> kept the girls awake.

e The howling made <u>the heads of the girls</u> hurt.

f There was wet paint on <u>the seats of the chairs</u>.

Remember

Not all plural owners end in **s**: men   mice

If the owner is plural and does not ends in **s**, add **'s**:

the **mice's** cage (the owners are two or more **mice**)

2 Rewrite these phrases using the possessive apostrophe.

a the advice of two wise people   *two wise people's advice*

b the library for children

c the food belonging to the mice

d the football team of women

e the field for the sheep

3 Put in the eight apostrophes that have been left out of this paragraph.

> Remember to put the apostrophe straight after the owner's name.

The childrens mouths hung open in shock.
What had happened to their houses door?
What was on the front windows glass?
How had the roofs tiles become blue?
Why were fishes tails flapping about?
Their parents work was behind this!
The partys theme was an
underwater adventure!

Give yourself a sticker

Check

Check that you know the three rules for placing apostrophes of possession.

Direct speech

1 Place the missing inverted commas in these sentences.

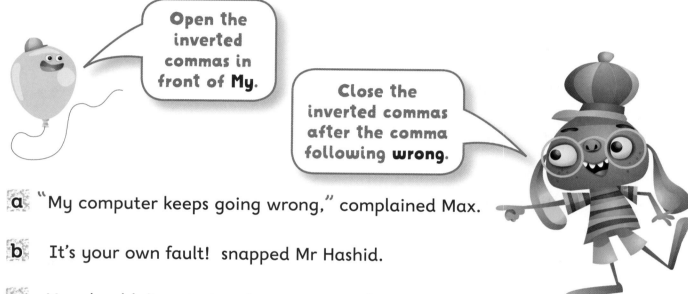

Open the inverted commas in front of **My**.

Close the inverted commas after the comma following **wrong**.

a "My computer keeps going wrong," complained Max.

b It's your own fault! snapped Mr Hashid.

c You shouldn't press two keys at once, he continued.

d My brother said that's a quick way to get things done, replied Max.

e Does your brother keep breaking computers as well? asked Mr Hashid.

2 Circle the five punctuation marks that divide the five sentences above.

3 Write Max's reply to Mr Hashid's question, using inverted commas and a punctuation mark that divides the sentence.

_____

_____

_____

4 Read what other children in Max's class said. Complete the last speech bubble yourself.

There's smoke coming out of the back!

Jacob

Do you know what you're doing?

Dwayne

I'm going to tell Mr Hashid.

Martha

Mia

Remember

The reporting clause that tells you who is speaking may come before the speech. The verb is followed by a comma.

Max mumbled, "People always blame me."

5 Write direct speech sentences using the words in the speech bubbles. Include more interesting words than 'said'. The words in the box may help.

shouted   declared   called   shrieked   demanded   murmured   quizzed   threatened

Jacob groaned, "There's smoke coming out of the back!"

Check

Have you always put inverted commas around the spoken words? Have you separated the two parts of the sentence?

Give yourself a sticker

Adverbs and adverbials

I'm thinking hard!

1 Circle the adverb in each sentence. Underline the verb it adds information to.

a The weather forecaster <u>looked</u> (anxiously) at the map.

b Strong winds appeared distantly.

c Viewers were relying completely on her information.

d She calculated speeds carefully.

e Qualified forecasters never guessed.

2 Sort the words in the box into their adverb categories and write them next to the question they answer.

> so   lightly   just   immediately   daily   nearby   later   softly
> there   often   heavily   extremely   locally   today   hourly

How? _____ _____ _____

When? _____ _____ _____

Where? _____ _____ _____

How often? _____ _____ _____

How much? _____ _____ _____

3 Circle the adverbial phrase in each sentence.

a The forecaster checked her numbers (over and over again.)

b She listed the measurements with great care.

c There was one result in the end.

d Wind speeds would peak at a dangerous level.

e A giant dust storm would occur in the afternoon.

4 Complete the paragraph with the adverbial phrases in the box.

in the local area	with care	within buildings
in a serious way	with speed	at regular intervals

DUST STORM ALERT!

The forecaster faced the cameras _____.

She spoke _____. Parents and

teachers must act _____. The dust

storm would occur _____. Adults must

check for updates _____. All children

must be kept _____.

Check
Check that you know what adverbs and adverbials are.
What information do they give? ☐

Adverbials at the start of sentences

Some people call this 'a fronted adverbial'.

1 Match the sentence halves.

At first	everyone watched the sky
With some fear	they thought about the danger
All the time	no one knew what to do

2 Write the sentences you have made. Put the adverbial at the start and use two punctuation marks in each sentence.

_____

_____

_____

3 Complete the weather story by finishing these sentences with your own words.

a All the time _____

b In a strange way _____

c With amazing speed _____

d By the end of the day _____

Check

Have you put a comma after the adverbial when it starts the sentence? ☐

Give yourself a sticker

Now – track how you're doing on page 31!

The suffix -ation

Remember
A **suffix** is a group of letters added to the **end** of a word to make a new word.

The suffix **-ation** is added to a verb to form a noun: inform + ation = information

Spelling changes may occur in the original word: adore + ation = adoration

1 Complete these suffix statements.

a sense + ation → _____

b admire + ation → _____

c relax + ation → _____

d reserve + ation → _____

e expect + ation → _____

f _____ + ation → conservation

g _____ + ation → preservation

h _____ + ation → valuation

> Don't forget to drop the e!

2 Match each word with the correct meaning.

conservation	leisure
expectation	worth
reservation	preserving
valuation	awaiting
relaxation	saved place

Check
Check that you know what happens when you add **-ation** to a verb ending in **e**. ☐

> Give yourself a sticker

Now – track how you're doing on page 31!

Homophones

1 Match the pairs of homophones.

you   grate   through   right   knight   eye

write   I   threw   night   ewe   great

2 Use **ewe** and **grate** in sentences.

_____

_____

_____

3 Circle the correct homophone in each of the sentences.

a I will **be / bee** late home today.

b I am going to my friend's **plaice / place**.

c We **might / mite** play on her computer.

d We will **see / sea** what we prefer.

e My mum will collect me at **for / four** o'clock.

Remember

Homophones are two or more words that sound the same but have different spellings and meanings.

Some words are near-homophones. They have different meanings and sound almost the same.

4 Find the sets of three homophones in this list. Write each set in a row.

| you | they're | rain | two | sent | ewe | reign | too |

| there | cent | to | yew | their | scent | rein |

you

5 Write meanings for the words **yew** and **ewe**.

Grab a dictionary if you need one!

Check

Check the meaning of any words you don't know, as this will help you remember the different ways of spelling the homophones.

Give yourself a sticker

Nouns and pronouns

Can you hear how the pronoun improves the flow of the sentences?

Remember

A noun is a word that names people, places or things:

| ball | Wayne |

A pronoun is a word that can replace a noun:

| it | he |

Using a pronoun avoids having to repeat names:

Wayne bought a **ball**. **He** bought **it** in the new sports shop.

---

1 Underline the noun in the first sentence and circle the pronoun that replaces it in the second sentence.

No boring repetition!

a Animals were arriving! They were coming soon.

b News travelled fast. It was soon everywhere.

c The elephant had trumpeted loudly. She had such a strong voice.

d Monkeys chattered excitedly. They hoped for another playmate.

e Only the giraffe was quiet. He was always shy.

Remember

These are called **personal** pronouns:

| it | we | I | you | they | he | she |

---

2 Write a personal pronoun in each space.

a Sophie, the head keeper, had asked for more giraffes and, as expected, _____ had arrived.

b Darren, the other keeper, moaned that _____ had wanted lions.

c Sophie got cross and said that _____ was senior to Darren.

d "_____ have to wait for your turn," said Sophie.

Remember

The **subject pronoun** is who or what the sentence is about.

> I went to the park.

> It went off with a bang.

The **object pronoun** is who or what is having something happen to them.

> Peter came to the park with **me**.

Subject pronouns are: **I, you, he, she, it, we, you, they.**

Object pronouns are: **me, you, him, her, it, us, you, them.**

3 Write the pronoun you can use to replace the noun in **bold** in each of the sentences.

a The animals all had labels on **the animals**. _____

b Sophie spotted labels addressed to **Sophie**. _____

c "Every giraffe is for **Sophie**!" shrieked Sophie. _____

d "Yes, so all the work is just for **Sophie** as well!" muttered Darren. _____

Remember

Possessive pronouns also replace nouns, but they show ownership:

| mine | yours | its | hers | his | ours | theirs |

4 Write a possessive pronoun in each gap.

a The two keepers pretended the park was _____.

b Sophie had her side of the park and Darren had _____.

c Darren worked with his animals and Sophie looked after _____.

d The park owner asked them furiously: "Was this idea _____?"

e "I am in charge", he continued, "so any changes will be _____."

f From then on, Mr Barnes made sure that the decisions were always _____.

Noun phrases

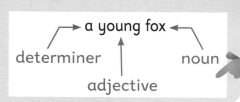

determiner → a young fox ← noun

adjective

A phrase is just part of a sentence – it doesn't make complete sense on its own.

1 Choose a determiner, a noun and another word to create five noun phrases to suit a mystery story about the fox.

Determiners

| a | an | the | some | that | those | this | these |

Adjectives

| cunning | old | young | dark | sudden | loud |

| hungry | mysterious |

Nouns

| rubbish | bin | fox | den | cubs | night | noise | shadow | vixen |

_____

_____

_____

_____

_____

2 Write two sentences for a mystery adventure story, including two of your noun phrases. Underline the noun phrases.

_____

_____

_____

Remember

A noun phrase can be extended by adding a preposition and another noun:

> a shadowy figure <u>on the path</u>
>
> determiner
>
> adjective   main noun   preposition + noun

3 Write four longer noun phrases, including words from each of these sets.

Determiners

a   the   some   that   those   this   these   one

Main nouns

bin   fox   den   cubs   night   noise   foxes   food   figure

Adjectives

young   dark   sudden   loud   hungry   shadowy   mysterious

frightening   large   moonlit   smelly

Prepositions with nouns

with a bushy tail   with a metal lid   without any stars

on the path   in the darkness   in the garden   under the trees

_____

_____

_____

_____

Give
yourself
a sticker

Check

Do you understand what a noun phrase is?

Do your sentences make complete sense?

Word families

Get ideas from the list of endings.

1 Choose four root words. Write as many new words as you can based on each root word.

Root words

| shop | look | harm | teach | farm | help | fish |

| care | write | work | hop | skip | speak | play |

Helpful word endings

| -er | -s | -es | -ing | -ed | -y | -ly | -ful | -fully |

_____ _____ _____ _____

_____ _____ _____ _____

_____ _____ _____ _____

_____ _____ _____ _____

2 Match the words that belong to the same word family.

invent   discovery

discover   exploration

neighbourhood   home

explore   neighbour

homeless   invention

Just let me think...

3 Create word families from these roots.

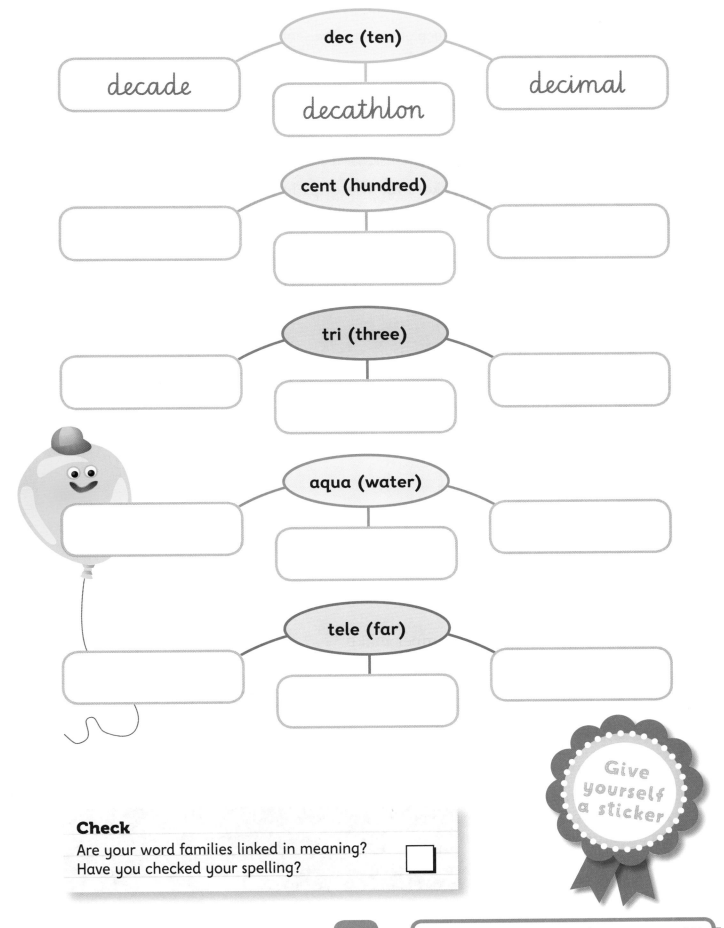

dec (ten)

decade

decathlon

decimal

cent (hundred)

tri (three)

aqua (water)

tele (far)

Check

Are your word families linked in meaning?
Have you checked your spelling?

Give yourself a sticker

Now – track how you're doing on page 31!

Paragraphs

Always start a new paragraph on a new line.

Remember

A paragraph is a section in a piece of writing. The sentences in it are usually all about the same thing.

In non-fiction texts, headings and subheadings may separate the paragraphs and make information easy to find.

1 Choose the correct stickers for the gaps in this page of information text.

> Main heading
>
> Subheading
>
> Spring covers three months of the year: March, April and May. The weather is changeable and is often windy. April is usually the wettest month.
>
> Subheading
>
> The second season in the year's cycle is summer. It is the warmest time of the year. It lasts from June to the end of August. It is a popular holiday time.
>
> Subheading
>
> September, October and November make up autumn. They are the months when daylight hours become shorter. Some trees lose their leaves.
>
> Subheading
>
> The last season is winter. December, January and February are the coldest months of the year. It may snow. Frosty, icy conditions are common.

Give yourself a sticker

Now – track how you're doing on page 31!

Progress chart

Colour in a face.

	I can do this well
	I can do this but need more practice
	I find this difficult

Page	I can . . .	How did you do?
2	I can distinguish between a plural **s** and a possessive **s**.	😊 😐 🙁
3–5	I can recognise the three sounds made by **ch**, sounds made by **y** and sounds made by **ou** in words.	😊 😐 🙁
6–7	I can use the prefixes **il-**, **ir-**, **inter-** and **super-** to create new words.	😊 😐 🙁
8–9	I can pronounce and use words ending in **-sure**, **-ture**, **-(t)cher** and **-cian**.	😊 😐 🙁
10–11	I can understand the rule for doubling a consonant when adding an ending that starts with a vowel.	😊 😐 🙁
12	I can hear the difference between words ending in **-gue** and **-que**.	😊 😐 🙁
13	I can hear the sound made by **ei** and **ey** and use the letter groups correctly.	😊 😐 🙁
14–15	I can use apostrophes to mark possession.	😊 😐 🙁
16–17	I can punctuate direct speech.	😊 😐 🙁
18–20	I can identify adverbs and adverbials and use the correct punctuation when starting sentences with adverbials.	😊 😐 🙁
21	I can form new words with the suffix **-ation**.	😊 😐 🙁
22–23	I can match homophones.	😊 😐 🙁
24–27	I can use pronouns to replace nouns, and explain and construct noun phrases.	😊 😐 🙁
28–29	I can identify words belonging to the same family.	😊 😐 🙁
30	I can use organisational devices.	😊 😐 🙁

How did YOU do?

Answers

PAGE 2

1 **a** possession
  b plural
  c possession
  d possession

2 **b** cats
  c hers
  d snakes
  e teacher's

PAGE 3

1 ch as in chat: chimney, cheese, lunch
  ch as in echo: chrome, character, school
  ch as in machine: brochure, chauffeur, parachute

2 and 3 Make sure your child understands the words.

PAGE 4

1 Check the words' spelling.

2 Make sure your child distinguishes between the **ee** and **igh** sounds.
  ee sound: lucky, funny, sorry
  igh sound: fly, cry, dry

3 myth – a story about gods and goddesses
  Egypt – an African country
  pyramid – a structure with a base and triangular, sloping sides
  mystery – a puzzle
  gym – an exercise room

PAGE 5

1 ou sound: round, sound
  oo sound: group, troupe

2 **a** the opposite of old – young
  b twice as much – double
  c put your hand on – touch
  d a mass of land – country
  e a bit of bother – trouble

PAGES 6–7

1 illegible, illogical, irrational, irrelevant, irregular, illiterate

2 words beginning with **il**: illegible, illogical, illiterate
  words beginning with **ir**: irrelevant, irrational, irregular

3 Words beginning with **l** use the prefix **il**; words beginning with **r** use the prefix **ir**.

4 Zog had amazing powers. His strength, greater than any ordinary person's, was **superhuman**. His booster rocket pack was **supercharged**, so that he could fly at **supersonic** speed. It was not surprising that others called him **superman**.

5 Check that your child understands the word.

6 international – between countries
  intercity – between cities
  interchange – a junction between roads
  interaction – communication between two people and their effect on each other
  intercom – system of radio communication between people

PAGES 8–9

1 words ending in -ture: furniture, picture, lecture
  words ending in -sure: measure, treasure, pleasure

2 **b** pleasure
  c pasture
  d leisure
  e adventure
  f creature

3 fracture, teacher, richer, stretcher, posture, catcher

4 Make sure your child understands the words.

5 The party entertainer was a **magician**. He could add up card numbers like a **mathematician**. Next, he turned himself into a computer **technician** and mended the children's laptop. Then, as a qualified **electrician**, he rewired everything and made keys glow and lights flash off and on!

PAGES 10–11

1 forg**et**, ref**it**, adm**it**, beg**in**

2 **a** forgetting
  b beginner
  c beginning
  d forgotten
  e preferred
  f preferring

3 Check your child uses the words appropriately.

4 gard**en** lim**it** nov**el** pard**on**

5 **a** gardener
  b novelist
  c gardening
  d trumpeter
  e limited
  f limitation

6 Check your child's spelling and use of the words.

PAGE 12

1 g sound: rogue, meringue, vague, plague
  k sound: cheque, technique, unique, arabesque

2 tongue, fatigue, dialogue, boutique, mosque, prologue

3 picturesque – making a striking picture

unique – the only one of its kind
arabesque – a ballet movement
antique – old-fashioned
mystique – atmosphere of mystery
opaque – cannot be seen through

PAGE 13

1 abseil, they, neigh, obey, prey

2 Check your child's use of these words and the marking of **ei** and **ey**.

PAGES 14–15

1 **b** The car's engine
  c The book's name
  d The dogs' noise
  e the girls' heads
  f the chairs' seats

2 **a** two wise people's advice
  b the children's library
  c the mice's food
  d the women's football team
  e the sheep's field

3 The children's mouths hung open in shock. What had happened to their house's door? What was on the front window's glass? How had the roof's tiles become blue? Why were fishes' tails flapping about? Their parents' work was behind this! The party's theme was an underwater adventure!

PAGES 16–17

1 and 2 **a** "My computer keeps going wrong," complained Max.
  b "It's your own fault," snapped Mr Hashid.
  c "You shouldn't press two keys at once," he continued.
  d "My brother said that's a quick way to get things done," replied Max.
  e "Does your brother keep breaking computers as well?" asked Mr Hashid.

3 Make sure your child uses correct punctuation.

4 Child's own writing

5 Example answers:
  "Do you know what you're doing?" quizzed Dwayne.
  "I'm going to tell Mr Hashid," threatened Martha.

PAGES 18–19

1 **b** Strong winds <u>appeared</u> (distantly)
  c Viewers <u>were relying</u> (completely) on her information.
  d She <u>calculated</u> speeds (carefully)
  e Qualified forecasters (never) <u>guessed</u>.